REVISE KEY STAGE 2 SATs
English

TARGETED PRACTICE READING

Series Consultant: Janice Pimm

Author: Catherine Baker

Also available:

Revise Key Stage 2 SATs English Targeted Practice
Spelling   9781292145969

Revise Key Stage 2 SATs English Targeted Practice
Grammar   9781292145945

For the full range of Pearson revision titles, visit:
www.pearsonschools.co.uk/revise

Contents

Introduction

About your tests

At the end of Year 6, you will take tests to find out about your English skills. This book will help you revise your **reading** skills. There will be one **reading** test. You will have to read three texts and answer questions about them. You will have 1 hour to do this test.

There will be also be one **grammar** test and one **spelling** test. Your teacher will look at some of your pieces of **writing** but there won't be a writing test.

Using this book

Each page of this book is about a different skill. Use the checkboxes at the top of the page to track your progress:

Had a go ☐ Tick this box when you've read the page.

Nearly there ☐ Tick this box when you understand the page quite well.

Nailed it! ☐ Tick this box when you understand the page really well.

Text 1: Fiction

The Scarecrow and his Servant by Philip Pullman

One day old Mr Pandolfo, who hadn't been feeling at all well, decided that it was time to make a scarecrow. The birds had been very troublesome.
Come to that, his rheumatism had been troublesome, and the soldiers had been troublesome, and the weather had been troublesome, and his cousins had been troublesome. It was all getting a bit too much for him. Even his old pet raven had flown away.

He couldn't do anything about his rheumatism, or the soldiers, or the weather, or his cousins, who were the biggest problem of all. There was a whole family of them, the Buffalonis, and they wanted to get hold of his land and divert all the springs and streams, and drain all the wells, and put up a factory to make weedkiller and rat poison and insecticide.

All those troubles were too big for old Mr Pandolfo to manage, but he thought he could do something about the birds, at least. So he put together a fine-looking scarecrow, with a big solid turnip for a head and a sturdy broomstick for a backbone, and dressed him in an old tweed suit, and stuffed him tightly with straw. Then he tucked a short letter inside him, wrapped in oilskin for safety.

'There you are,' he said. 'Now you remember what your job is, and remember where you belong. Be courteous, and be brave, and be honourable, and be kind. And the best of blooming luck.'

He stuck the scarecrow in the middle of the wheatfield, and went home to lie down, because he wasn't feeling well at all.

That night another farmer came along and stole the scarecrow, being too lazy to make one himself. And the next night someone else came along and stole him again.

So little by little the scarecrow moved away from the place where he was made, and he got more and more tattered and torn, and finally he didn't look nearly as smart as he'd done when Mr Pandolfo put him together. He stood in the middle of a muddy field, and he stayed there.

But one night there was a thunderstorm. It was a very violent one, and everyone in the district shivered and trembled and jumped as the thunder went off like cannon-fire and the lightning lashed down like whips. The scarecrow stood there in the wind and the rain, taking no notice.

And so he might have stayed; but then there came one of those million-to-one chances that are like winning the lottery. All his molecules and atoms and elementary particles and whatnot were lined up in exactly the right way to switch on when the lightning struck him, which it did at two in the morning, fizzing its way through his turnip and down his broomstick and into the mud.

The Scarecrow blinked with surprise and looked all around. There wasn't much to see except a field of mud, and not much light to see it by except the flashes of lightning.

Still, there wasn't a bird in sight.
'Excellent,' said the Scarecrow.

Retrieval

1. What is the problem with Mr Pandolfo's pet raven?

For retrieval questions, the answer is there in the text! You just have to read carefully to find it.

Tick **one.**

It is eating Mr Pandolfo's crops. ☐

The soldiers have taken it. ☐

It has flown away. ☐

It has gone to live with the Buffalonis. ☐

1 mark

2. Circle the correct option to complete each sentence.

   a) The main thing worrying Mr Pandolfo is…

   the birds.   his rheumatism.   the soldiers.   his relatives.   **1 mark**

   b) The scarecrow's spine is made from…

   a turnip.   a broomstick.   tweed.   straw.   **1 mark**

   c) When the thunderstorm came, at first the scarecrow…

   took no notice.   was terrified.   was happy.   was worried. **1 mark**

3. How does the scarecrow end up a long way from Mr Pandolfo's field?

   ....

   ....   **1 mark**

Retrieval

1. Explain what happens to the scarecrow when the storm takes place.

....

....

Sometimes retrieval questions use words that aren't in the text. Think about what the question is asking you, and then look for the answer.

.... **1 mark**

2. Find and copy the sentence in paragraph 3 that tells you why Mr Pandolfo decides to make the scarecrow.

....

.... **1 mark**

3. In your own words, give two reasons why the Buffalonis are a problem for Mr Pandolfo.

....

....

....

.... **2 marks**

Inference

1. Do you think this story takes place in wartime or peacetime? Use evidence from the text to support your answer.

....

....

....

> You need to put together clues from the text, and from what you already know, to answer inference questions. Don't expect the answer to be right there in the text!

2 marks

2. What is the most likely reason why the scarecrow stays put in the muddy field in paragraph 7 (beginning 'So little by little...')?

Tick **one**.

It is too tired to move. ☐

It is so tatty that no one else steals it. ☐

It knows Mr Pandolfo wanted it to stay there. ☐

It likes living in the field. ☐

1 mark

3. How do you think Mr Pandolfo feels when he finds out that his scarecrow is gone? Use evidence from the text to support your answer.

....

....

....

.... **2 marks**

Inference

1.

| 'Excellent,' said the Scarecrow. |

Why do you think the Scarecrow says this? Use evidence from the text
to support your answer.

....

....

.... 2 marks

2. What kind of person is Mr Pandolfo? Write
a paragraph describing him. Include at least
three points about Mr Pandolfo in
your answer. Use evidence from the text
to support your answer.

Question 2 asks you
to use ideas from the story
to work out as much as
possible about Mr Pandolfo.
What does the story tell us
about him and what can we
work out from the things
he says and does?

....

....

....

....

....

.... 3 marks

3. What is different about the way the word 'scarecrow' is written in the
last three paragraphs and the way it is written earlier in the story?
Why do you think the author has done this?

....

....

.... 2 marks

6

Word meanings

1.

> So he put together a fine-looking scarecrow, with a big solid turnip for a head and a sturdy broomstick for a backbone...

When working out word meanings, try swapping the words in the answers for the word in the text. This can help you work out which of the alternatives is best.

In this sentence, the word 'sturdy' is closest in meaning to...

Tick **one**.

thick. ☐

strong. ☐

slender. ☐

broken. ☐

1 mark

2. Draw lines to match the words from the text with their meanings.

tweed	poison to kill pests
turnip	polite
courteous	thick woollen material
insecticide	a root vegetable

2 marks

3. Complete the table by writing a definition for each word from the story.

word	definition
troublesome	
tattered	
shivered	

3 marks

Language for effect

1. Find and copy a simile in the story, and explain why it is effective.

   ....

   ....

   ....

> These questions ask you to think about why the author has used language in a certain way. Think about the effect the language has on you as you read – does it make you laugh, feel sorry for a character, feel nervous or something else?

2 marks

2.

> 'Be courteous, and be brave, and be honourable, and be kind. And the best of blooming luck.'

Explain the effect the last sentence has on the reader. Use evidence from the text to support your answer.

   ....

   ....

   ....   2 marks

3. What word has the author chosen to repeat several times in paragraph 1? In your own words, explain the effect of this repetition.

   ....

   ....

   ....   2 marks

Text 2: Newspaper article

23rd August   **The News**   Sport

Shooting star:
Eniola Aluko

It's an exciting time for women's football. After the Great Britain women's team reached the quarter-finals at the 2012 London Olympics, lots of people started to realise that women's football could be just as skilful, thrilling and fun to watch as men's. Then the England women's team reached the semi-finals of the World Cup in 2015, outperforming the men, and suddenly it's begun to look as though women's football is finally getting the attention it deserves.

One keenly-watched star of the women's game is Chelsea and England striker Eniola Aluko. Still only 29, she's already been playing seriously for a long time – she was the Football Association's Young Player of the Year in 2003, and sat her history A Level exam just hours before she played against Denmark in the 2005 European championships.

Eniola played in the London Olympics in 2012, and in 2015 she helped her team, Chelsea, win the Women's Super League and FA Cup double – making it a real year to remember. But as for so many other women's football stars, getting to the top in her chosen profession hasn't been easy.
Quite apart from the athleticism, energy and drive required by any top-level footballer, women in football face additional barriers that don't necessarily affect the stars of the men's game.

23rd August   **The News**   Sport

Eniola's brother Sone is also a star striker: he was spotted by Birmingham City at just eight years old, and has played for Aberdeen and Rangers as well as his current club, Hull City. Sone has always been a professional footballer, but when Eniola was starting out in the sport, professional football wasn't even an option for women players, because women's teams couldn't afford to pay them a full-time salary. As a result, Eniola had to have a back-up plan, so she studied hard and qualified as a lawyer, ending up working with big names like One Direction and David Beckham. It was always tricky balancing studying and working as a lawyer with football, and it wasn't until 2014 that Eniola was able to give up law and play football full-time for Chelsea.

But Eniola isn't bitter. As she says, having a back-up plan is never a bad thing, and her law background may stand her in good stead when her football career's over. Meanwhile, she's fully aware of the value of what football has taught her. "What sport does is give you those experiences – which are real. You are going to fail in sport, you are going to win sometimes, you are going to be criticised sometimes, you are going to be applauded – so it gives you ... well, it's certainly given me anyway, those real-life lessons that make you bulletproof."

Factfile:

Eniola Aluko

- Born in 1987 in Lagos, Nigeria
- Moved to Birmingham, England at 6 months old
- Proudest footballing moment: winning the FA Cup at Wembley, 2015, and being selected as player of the match
- Current team: Chelsea Ladies

Retrieval

1. **Which is the earliest of Eniola's achievements that the text tells us about?**

   *You need to think about the **dates** of each of the events listed.*

   Tick **one.**

   playing against Denmark in the European championships ☐

   playing in the London Olympics ☐

   starting to play full-time for Chelsea ☐

   becoming the FA's Young Player of the Year ☐

   1 mark

2. **Circle the correct option to complete each sentence.**

   a) In the 2015 World Cup, the England women's team...

   did better than the men.

   failed to qualify.

   won the World Cup.

   lost to Denmark.

   1 mark

   b) As a lawyer, Eniola has...

   worked with One Direction.

   represented her brother Sone.

   given up football.

   1 mark

3. **Re-read the first page of *Shooting Star: Eniola Aluko*. Which two events does the text say helped women's football to get more attention?**

   ....

   ....

   ....

   .... 2 marks

Retrieval

1. Tick one box in each row to show
   which statements are true and
   which are false.

> Remember to read the
> text carefully! You don't need to use
> inference or your own imagination to
> answer these questions.

statement	true	false
Eniola's brother, Sone, has been a professional footballer for longer than she has.		
Eniola plays for Hull City.		
Eniola originally trained as a lawyer because she didn't want to play football full-time.		
Eniola played against Denmark when she was still at school.		

2 marks

2. Find and copy the sentence on page 10 that tells you why Eniola isn't
   sorry she trained as a lawyer.

   ....

   .... 1 mark

3.

> ...women in football face additional barriers that don't necessarily affect the
> stars of the men's game.

What is the main barrier for women in football that the text tells us about?
Explain why this doesn't affect men in the same way.

   ....

   ....

   ....

   .... 2 marks

Inference

1.

> It was always tricky balancing studying and working as a lawyer with football.

What is the most likely reason why this was tricky?

> You need to think about Eniola and her situation. In questions like this, more than one of the answers might be true for some people, but only one of them is true for Eniola.

Tick **one.**

Most people are not good both at studying and at football. ☐

Both football and studying are very time-consuming and tiring. ☐

Eniola's parents did not want her to be a footballer. ☐

Lawyers are not allowed to play football. ☐

1 mark

2. **In what way does Eniola suggest football has given her 'real life lessons'? Use evidence from the text to support your answer.**

....

.... 2 marks

3. a) **Which of the words below best describes Eniola's personality?**

Tick **one.**

determined ☐

fame-hungry ☐

cautious ☐

dramatic ☐

1 mark

b) **Explain why you chose this word to describe Eniola. Use evidence from the text to support your answer.**

....

....

.... 2 marks

Make connections

1. What are the most likely reasons why the writer included information about Eniola's brother Sone in the article?

> These questions ask you to think about how the different parts of the text work together to give information. Think about the jobs that the different parts of the text do and **why** the writer might have used them.

Tick **two.**

It's interesting and unusual that brother and sister are both footballers. ☐

Men's football is more popular than women's football so the author wanted to include a man. ☐

Sone's experience shows how things are different for men than for women in football. ☐

Sone taught Eniola how to play football. ☐

2 marks

2. Why do you think the author included a fact file about Eniola? Explain what it adds to the text.

....

.... 1 mark

3. Find and copy one sentence that is a quotation from Eniola. In your own words, explain why you think the writer chose to use Eniola's own words rather than summarising what she said.

....

....

....

....

.... 2 marks

Word meanings

1.

> Quite apart from the athleticism, energy and drive required by any top-level footballer, women in football face additional barriers that don't necessarily affect the stars of the men's game.

In this sentence, the word 'drive' is closest in meaning to...

Tick **one.**

> Sometimes words can have more than one meaning. For these questions, you need to think about what each word means in **this** text.

travel. ☐

direction. ☐

determination. ☐

life. ☐

1 mark

2. Circle the word or phrase that is closest in meaning to each word from the text.

a) outperforming

doing better than   acting   pretending

b) balancing

teetering   combining   varying

c) face

expression   hope for   have to put up with   **3 marks**

3. Complete the table by finding and copying a word from the text that matches each definition.

definition	word from the text
exciting and enjoyable	
difficulties that prevent people achieving a goal	
money earned for doing a job	
notice taken of someone or something	

2 marks

Summarise

1. Re-read paragraph 2 (beginning 'One keenly-watched star...'). Which of the headings below would best sum up the main point of this paragraph?

*Texts often include a lot of information – some of it very important and some less so! These questions ask you to think about just the **main** message of the text.*

Tick **one.**

Young Player of the Year   ☐

Early Career   ☐

Working Hard for Exams   ☐

European Champion   ☐

1 mark

2. Re-read paragraph 4 (beginning 'Eniola's brother Sone...'). Write one sentence to sum up the main message given in this paragraph.

....

....

.... 1 mark

3. a) In one sentence, sum up the most important message the article gives us about Eniola.

....

....

   b) In one sentence, sum up what the article tells us about women's football in general.

....

.... 2 marks

16

Text 3: Poem

Mapping Our World

The stream. Our special place,
In a tangle of woods
At the edge of the park.
It flowed through our childhood,
Ripple-voiced, light-darting,
With minnows in the shallows,
Mind-monsters in the deeps.
We followed it, mapped it,
Named its broads and narrows,
Its dams, falls and pools,
Waded, splashed, climbed, fished,
Knew the deep slow places under trees,
The soft mud that sucked at our legs,
The small Niagara where leaves rode the rapids,
The creaking branch, a bridge
For teetering tightrope-walkers,
The spangled moss-green cushion,
The lurking crocodile log.

We knew that scattered acorn-cups
Held drinks for fairies,
And that hazelnuts
Were nibbled by tiny teeth.
We knew the magic there
Would shimmer and dazzle
If only we could come by moonlight,
To see what crept from the mudbank
Abseiled from the trees
And danced in the shadows
Enchanting the fish.

While we whispered plans and secrets
The grown-ups shared flasks and gossip.
Answering their call, we came at last
Across the grass, wild with adventure,
Mud-streaked, moss-flecked, twig-snagged,
Story-mazed, stream-charmed,
And pitied them –

For their world
So much smaller than ours.
Linda Newbery

Retrieval

1. Tick one box in each row to show which statements are true and which are false.

For these questions, you need to think about the **surface** meaning of the poem and look for information that is right there in the text.

statement	true	false
The stream described in the poem was near a park.		
There was a crocodile in the stream.		
There were fish in the stream.		
The children often got messy when they played by the stream.		
The children were not allowed to play in the mud.		
The children often visited the stream during the night.		

3 marks

2. What did the children use to help them get across the stream?

....

.... 1 mark

3. What two things were the grown-ups doing when the children were playing by the stream?

....

.... 2 marks

19

Inference

1.

> The spangled moss-green cushion...

Which of the following is the 'moss-green cushion' most likely to be?

In poems, we often have to use inference to help us imagine the scene being described. The poem doesn't necessarily describe what is happening in a straightforward way, so you have to think about what the poet **might** mean.

Tick **one.**

an old chair someone has dumped in the stream ☐

a branch across the stream ☐

a stone covered with soft moss ☐

a cushion left behind by the fairies ☐

1 mark

2.

> Mind-monsters in the deeps.

In your own words, explain what you think the 'mind-monsters' are. Use evidence from the poem to support your answer.

....

....

.... 2 marks

3. Do you think the narrator of the poem is a child, or an adult looking back at the past? Explain why you think this. Use evidence from the text to support your answer.

....

....

....

.... 2 marks

20

Inference

1.

> The small Niagara where leaves rode the rapids...

You need to think about the meaning of 'Niagara' and 'rapids'.

What does this line tell us about the stream?

Tick **one.**

There were trees nearby with leaves big enough to ride on. ☐

It was very narrow. ☐

It was in Canada. ☐

It had a little waterfall or a place where the water moved quickly. ☐

1 mark

2. Who do you think the 'teetering tightrope-walkers' were? Why do you think the author has used these words to describe them?

....

....

.... 2 marks

3.

> ...And pitied them - / For their world / So much smaller than ours.

Why do you think the children pitied the grown-ups? Do you agree with them? Explain why or why not. Use evidence to support your answer.

....

....

....

....

.... 3 marks

Word meanings

1. Circle the word or phrase that is closest in meaning to each word from the text.

> Poems often use unusual or imaginative words. If you're not sure what a word means, think about the meaning of the lines around the word and see if you can work it out from there.

a) minnows

   ripples   younger children   fish

b) lurking

   sulking   lying in wait   circling round and round

c) waded

   walked through water   swam   jumped   **3 marks**

2.
> We followed it, mapped it,
> Named its broads and narrows…

In this sentence, the word 'broads' is closest in meaning to…

Tick **one.**

places where the stream bends ☐
places where the stream is narrow ☐
places where the stream is wide ☐
places where the stream runs over rocks ☐   **1 mark**

3. Complete the table by finding and copying a word from the text that matches each definition.

definition	word from the text
places where the water is not very deep	
things all twisted together	
making a scraping or squeaking sound	
eaten with tiny bites	

2 marks

Language for effect

1. Find and copy two lines from the poem that use alliteration. Underline the letters that show alliteration.

> Poems often use imagery and descriptive language to help the reader imagine the scene. They may also use other effects, such as repetition, rhyme, rhythm and alliteration.

....

.... 2 marks

2.

> It flowed through our childhood,
> Ripple-voiced, light-darting...

Explain what the words 'Ripple-voiced' and 'light-darting' suggest about the stream.

....

....

.... 2 marks

3. Find and copy one or two lines in the poem where the author has used a list for effect. Explain what effect you think the writer has created. Give reasons for your answer.

....

....

....

.... 3 marks

Summarise

1. Re-read the poem from the beginning to 'Enchanting the fish.' Write one sentence to explain the main message of this part of the poem.

This poem has a lot of detail, but these questions ask you to think about the main messages of the poem.

....

....

.... 1 mark

2. Why do you think this poem is called *Mapping Our World?*

....

....

.... 1 mark

3. Think of a new title for the poem. Your title should reflect the mood and events in the poem.

.... 1 mark

4. What do you think is the main message the poet would like the reader to take away from the whole poem?

....

....

.... 1 mark

Text 4: Fiction

The River Singers by Tom Moorhouse

The dawn was grey and the waters quiet. Sylvan was the first awake, lying with his brother and sisters in a pile of cosily intertwined limbs. Their breathing lulled him even as lightness spread up the tunnel and into the chamber, bringing with it the scent of morning. He yawned. He opened his eyes. He grinned. Today was the day. At last.

Sylvan extracted himself, ignoring the others' sleepy protests, and sat with twitching whiskers at the entrance to the chamber. He should wait for them, he knew. They were supposed to go out all together. But the air stirred with a promise of new things and, with a final glance at his siblings, he stole away down the tunnel, paws padding on the soil. He had known the way for ages now. A left, a right, loop around a knot of roots, then pause at the place where the roof had fallen. One eye to the sky. Quiver. Listen. Check the scents. Then onwards and downwards to the lower places, the entrance to the Great River and the gateway to the world.

With each downward step the light grew brighter and the air fresher, more exhilarating. Another turn, a slight rise. And there she was: the Great River. Her waters, lapping against the family's trampled little platform, were bright through the shade of the tall grasses. She filled him with her vastness, her movement, her song. He felt the stirrings of hunger, the desire to dive, to twist, to flow with her. He hesitated, one forefoot raised, everything urging him out and into the world.

'And what exactly do you think you're doing, young vole?'

A paw was on his tail, pinning it to the floor.

Sylvan froze. He placed his foot hurriedly back onto the ground. As his mother removed her paw he turned, radiating guilt.

'Nothing.'

Her whiskers were stiff with disapproval. 'What have I told you about coming here?'

Sylvan dropped his gaze. 'I'm not allowed to. It's dangerous on my own,' he recited.

'That's right. So what are you doing?'

'Just looking.'

'Hmm. Well, that's just as well. Because any of my offspring stupid enough to think that he could go off exploring on his own would find himself in here gnawing nettle roots while the rest of us were outside. Understood, Sylvan?'

'Yes, Mother. Sorry.'

'I should think so. She surveyed the dejected water vole in front of her. 'I tell you what: since it's a nice calm day, and seeing as I promised, I don't see why we can't still have that little trip out. Together.' Sylvan's head came up. 'Really?'

'Really. Now why don't you go and wake the others?'

'Yes, Mother. It's –' He was almost dancing on the spot, torn between his desire to stay near the water and the rush to fetch his siblings.

She turned. 'What, dear?'

'It's wonderful,' he blurted.

She smiled, showing her strong, orange teeth. 'Yes, dear, it is. Now go.'

Retrieval

1. What kind of creature is Sylvan?

Tick **one.**

a water vole ☐

a mole ☐

a human ☐

The text doesn't tell us. ☐

Sometimes more than one option in a multiple choice question sounds likely. You have to read the text carefully to find out which is right.

1 mark

2. Circle the correct option to complete each sentence.

   a) When the story starts, it is...

   early morning.   very cold.

   breakfast time.   Sylvan's bedtime.   **1 mark**

   b) When Sylvan leaves the chamber, his brother and sisters...

   stay fast asleep.   complain sleepily.

   creep out too.   tell their mother.   **1 mark**

   c) Sylvan is just about to go out on the river bank when...

   his mother catches him.   it starts raining.

   the river floods.   he changes his mind.   **1 mark**

3. Why does Sylvan feel guilty when he sees his mother?

   ....

   ....

   .... **1 mark**

Retrieval

1. Complete the table by ticking one box in each row to show which statements are true, false or unknown.

statement	true	false	unknown
Sylvan doesn't know which way to go to get out on to the river bank.			
There are several different tunnels leading to the river.			
Sylvan's instinct is to be cautious about the river.			
The area where Sylvan sleeps is called the chamber.			
Sylvan has a long, thin, scaly tail.			
Sylvan's mother's teeth are orange.			

3 marks

2. Find and copy the sentence that tells you how Sylvan's mother feels when she sees him by the river.

....

.... 1 mark

3. Write a paragraph describing the setting of this story. Use evidence from the text to help you write your description.

....

....

....

Look carefully for information about the story setting within the text. Look for details that show where the story takes place, what the atmosphere is like and what the sounds, sights and smell are like.

....

....

.... 3 marks

Inference

1. Based on what you know or can work out from the text, which is the best description of Sylvan's mother?

Tick **one**.

strict and stern, without much sense of humour ☐

sometimes strict, but she wants her children to stay safe and have fun ☐

very anxious, wanting to keep her children safe at all times ☐

changes her mind a lot and doesn't mind what her children get up to ☐

> When answering inference questions, you often need to look for information from more than one point in the text. You also need to use your own knowledge of how people behave and how things work.

1 mark

2.

> He placed his foot hurriedly back onto the ground.

What is the most likely reason why Sylvan does this?

Tick **one**.

He is about to fall over. ☐

He doesn't want his mother to know that he was about to go outside. ☐

He wants his mother to take her paw off his foot. ☐

He is just about to run back inside the burrow. ☐

1 mark

3.

> He grinned. Today was the day. At last.

In your own words, explain why Sylvan is so excited when he wakes up.

....

....

.... **1 mar**

Inference

1. Do you think Sylvan's mother believes him when he says he's 'Just looking'? Explain your reasons. Use evidence from the text to support your answer.

....

....

.... **2 marks**

2.

> Sylvan extracted himself, ignoring the others' sleepy protests...

Why do you think Sylvan's brother and sisters protest?

....

....

.... **1 mark**

3. Write a character profile of Sylvan, including information about his appearance, his personality and his relationship with his family. You should write at least three sentences.

Think about what you can tell about Sylvan's personality from the way he acts. Look out for evidence in the text about how Sylvan gets on with his mother, brother and sisters too.

....

....

....

....

....

.... **3 marks**

Word meanings

1.

> She surveyed the dejected water vole in front of her.

In this sentence, the word 'dejected' is closest in meaning to...

Tick **one**.

Some words have more than one meaning, so you need to check carefully what the words mean in **this** text.

sad. ☐

distracted. ☐

guilty. ☐

angry. ☐

1 mark

2. Draw lines to match the words with their meanings as they are used in the text.

intertwined		crept quietly
lulled		twisted together
stole		looked at
surveyed		calmed

2 marks

3. Complete the table by writing a definition for each word as it is used in the text.

word	definition
hesitated	
vastness	
stirred	

3 marks

Prediction

1. What do you think Sylvan will say to his brother and sisters when he wakes them up? Write your prediction of what Sylvan might say, and how one of them might reply.

> You need to think about what you know about the characters from the story. You should think about what they are **likely** to do or say, and what is **likely** to happen.

....

....

....

....   2 marks

2. What do you think will happen when Sylvan and his family go on their trip? Write a paragraph describing what might happen. Use evidence from the text to support your answer.

....

....

....

....

....

....   3 marks

Text 5: Information text

Why do people cry?

Babies, children and adults – everyone cries sometimes! It's normal to cry when you are in pain or upset – and sometimes people also cry when they are very happy, or when watching a sad film, or even just when something gets into their eyes.
So what is crying and why do we do it?

Why do tears come out of our eyes?

Our eyes actually produce three different kinds of tears.

- Basal tears are always present in our eyes, stopping them drying out and keeping them healthy.

- Reflex tears are the ones we produce when our eyes are irritated, for example by smoke, chopping onions, or a stuck eyelash.

- Emotional tears are the ones we produce when we are sad or happy.

There's an obvious physical reason for basal and reflex tears – if we didn't produce them, our eyes would dry up and get sore. The reasons for emotional tears are a bit less obvious!

Why do we cry when we're sad?

Most scientists agree that crying can be a way of asking for help from other people. It is a sign of helplessness or vulnerability. So if you cry when you're sad, it's a way of saying, 'Come and help me.'

Lots of animals make loud sounds when something is wrong – but humans are among the few animals that produce tears when they are emotionally upset. One theory to explain why we cry quietly rather than yelling when upset is that loud noises can be dangerous – they could attract predators as well as your mum! So there's an evolutionary advantage in sending a signal for help quietly. As long as there are people close enough to see your tears, you will probably get the help you need without ending up as dinner for a predator.

Emotional tears are different from the other two types of tears in that they contain much higher levels of stress hormones – the chemicals in our bodies that make us feel on edge. Some people think crying is a way of getting rid of some of these stress hormones so that we're more relaxed. Whether this is true or not, many studies show that crying makes people feel better, so it does seem to reduce stress in some way.

Why do we sometimes cry when we're happy?

The hypothalamus, which is the part of the brain that transmits the signals to start off the crying process, can't tell the difference between one strong emotion and another. So tears can be triggered by strong happy emotions just as easily as by sad ones.

Just as tears of sadness send a signal to other people, so do tears of joy – so perhaps they developed as a way of communicating these strong happy emotions. Tears of happiness can also help to strengthen connections between people. For example, if we're both crying at the same happy thing, we feel that we've got something in common. Connections between people are important because they keep society working peacefully. So there could be an evolutionary advantage to these sorts of tears too.

Retrieval

1. Basal tears are different from the other types of tears mentioned because...

Tick **one.**

we've always got them in our eyes. ☐

they are not caused by emotion. ☐

they happen when we get something in our eyes. ☐

babies, children and adults can all have them. ☐

> Think about how basal tears are **different** from the other types of tears mentioned in the text.

1 mark

2. Circle the best option to complete each sentence.

a) If you get a piece of grit in your eye, you will probably cry...

basal tears.   emotional tears.   reflex tears.   1 mark

b) Unlike other types of tears, emotional tears contain high levels of...

stress hormones.   salt.   water.   1 mark

c) If we didn't produce basal tears, our eyes...

wouldn't see so well.   would get dry and sore.

wouldn't show others how we feel.   1 mark

3. In your own words, explain what 'evolutionary advantage' there might be...

a) for tears of sadness.

....

....

b) for tears of joy.

....

.... 2 marks

35

Inference

1.

> The reasons for emotional tears are a bit less obvious!

Why do you think the writer says this?

....

.... 1 mark

2. Do you think it is known for certain that crying helps us get rid of stress hormones so we feel more relaxed? Explain why you think this. Use evidence from the text to support your answer.

> Look for clues in the text that help you work out whether it's **definitely** known that crying gets rid of stress hormones.

....

....

.... 2 marks

3. Describe one situation in which you might cry reflex tears and explain how the tears would be helpful.

....

....

....

.... 2 marks

Word meanings

1. Draw lines to match the words with their meanings as they are used in the text.

present		set off or started

irritated		inflamed or sore

produce		there in a particular place

triggered		create or make

2 marks

2.

> The hypothalamus, which is the part of the brain that transmits the signals to start off the crying process, can't tell the difference between one strong emotion and another.

In this sentence, the word 'transmits' is closest in meaning to...

Tick **one.**

creates. ☐

explains. ☐

travels. ☐

sends. ☐

Non-fiction texts sometimes contain technical words that are needed to explain the topic. If you don't already know the meaning of these words, read the surrounding text to help you work out the most likely meaning.

1 mark

3. Complete the table by finding and writing a word from the text that has a similar meaning to each word or phrase shown below.

word or phrase	word from the text
weakness	
sad or worried	
calm	
conveying	

2 marks

Make connections

1. a) What do all the headings in this text have in common?

....

> For these questions, think about the information that the different parts of the text give you and how they all work together to help you build up a picture of the topic.

   b) Do you think headings like this are effective? Explain your reasons.

....

....

....

.... **3 marks**

2. a) Find the bullet points in the text. What information is given in this section?

....

....

   b) Why do you think the author chose to use bullet points in this section and not elsewhere?

....

....

.... **2 marks**

3. a) Re-read the first paragraph. What is the purpose of this section?

....

....

   b) How effectively do you think this section fulfils its purpose? Why do you think this?

....

....

.... **4 marks**

Summarise

1. Which of the headings below would make the best alternative title, summing up the whole text and striking the right tone?

> To pick an appropriate heading you need to think about the tone of the text as well as its content. For example, if it's a funny piece then a funny title would be appropriate; if it's serious, then it needs a serious title.

Tick **one.**

The Reasons for Our Tears ☐

Emotional Tears ☐

Boo Hoo! ☐

Cry Babies ☐

1 mark

2. Re-read the paragraph beginning 'Lots of animals...' and write one sentence to summarise the main idea in this paragraph.

....

....

.... **1 mark**

3. Re-read the section headed 'Why do we sometimes cry when we're happy?' and write one sentence to summarise the main idea in this section.

....

....

.... **1 mark**

Answers

TEXT 1: FICTION

Retrieval (page 3)

1. It has flown away.
2. *a)* his relatives.
   b) a broomstick.
   c) took no notice.
3. Several different people stole the scarecrow from each other so it moved from farm to farm, getting further away.

Retrieval (page 4)

1. The scarecrow is struck by lightning and comes to life.
2. 'All those troubles were too big for old Mr Pandolfo to manage, but he thought he could do something about the birds, at least.'
3. Accept any answer in the student's own words making any two of the following points: The Buffalonis wanted to take Mr Pandolfo's land away from him, they wanted to divert the springs and streams, they wanted to build a factory to make weedkiller and poisons.

Inference (page 5)

1. Probably wartime, because the story refers to soldiers being troublesome. (Award one mark for credible inference, one for referring back to the story for evidence.)
2. It is so tatty that no one else steals it.
3. Accept any credible answer that refers back to the text, e.g. 'Mr Pandolfo would feel upset because he had made the scarecrow to solve his problem with the birds, and also he told the scarecrow to 'remember what your job is, and remember where you belong". (Award one mark for credible inference, one for referring back to the story for evidence.)

Inference (page 6)

1. Accept any credible answer that makes sense within the story context, e.g. 'He is glad to be alive. He is glad there aren't any birds around for him to scare'.
2. Accept any accurately written paragraph that includes at least three different pieces of information about Mr Pandolfo, referring back to the text, e.g. 'We know that Mr Pandolfo is an old man and he is unwell. He is sensible and tries to solve his own problems (as we can see from the fact he makes the scarecrow). He is the kind of person who tries to do a good job, because he makes the scarecrow out of strong and sturdy materials. He might be imaginative, because he talks to the scarecrow even though it's not alive'.
3. 'Scarecrow' has an initial capital S at the end of the story, but lower case earlier in the story. Accept any answer that makes sense in the context, e.g. 'The scarecrow becomes 'Scarecrow' when he comes alive – so Scarecrow is like a person's name, whereas 'scarecrow' is just a description'. (Award one mark for identifying the difference, one for explaining it credibly.)

Word meanings

1. strong.

2. tweed: thick woollen material
   turnip: a root vegetable
   courteous: polite
   insecticide: poison to kill pests
3. Accept any accurate definition of the words as used in the text, e.g. troublesome: causing difficulty, tattered: ragged or torn, shivered: shook as if with cold or fear.

Language for effect

1. Accept either of the two similes in the story: 'thunder went off like cannon-fire', or 'lightning lashed down like whips'. Accept any reasonable explanation of why the chosen simile is effective. (Award one mark for identifying a simile, one for explaining why it is effective.)
2. Accept any reasoned response that is in keeping with the story, e.g. 'The last sentence is funny and effective, because the sentence before is quite solemn, but the last sentence uses the word 'blooming', which sounds slightly grumpy and very informal'. (Award one mark for identifying an effect on the reader, one for explaining how the effect is gained'.)
3. The repeated word is 'troublesome'. Accept any reasoned response explaining its effectiveness, e.g. 'It's effective because it makes you feel Mr Pandolfo has a long list of troubles', or 'It's not effective because it makes all the troubles sound the same and rather boring'. (Award one mark for identifying the repeated word; one for explaining the effect of repetition.)

TEXT 2: NEWSPAPER ARTICLE

Retrieval (page 11)

1. becoming the FA's Young Player of the Year
2. *a)* did better than the men.
   b) worked with One Direction.
3. Reaching the quarter-finals at the 2012 Olympics, and reaching the semi-finals of the 2015 World Cup.

Retrieval (page 12)

1. true, false, false, true
2. 'As she says, having a back-up plan is never a bad thing, and her law background may stand her in good stead when her football career's over.'
3. Accept an answer in the student's own words identifying that the main barrier for women is that it hasn't been easy for them to work as full-time professional players because clubs couldn't afford to pay them; this doesn't affect men in the same way because men's clubs have been able to pay them a salary.

Inference

1. Both football and study are very time-consuming and tiring.
2. Accept any reasoned answer that refers to the text, e.g. 'She says that in sport, sometimes you win and sometimes you are criticised, so she probably feels that football helps you to accept the ups and downs of life and be realistic'. (Award one mark for identifying the lessons, one for relating these back to life.)

Answers

3. a) determined

   b) Accept any reasoned explanation of why this word applies to Eniola, with evidence from the text, e.g. 'She must have been determined because she had to study hard and train as a lawyer at the same time as working hard on her football'. (Award one mark for credible inference, one for referring back to the text for evidence.)

Make connections

1. It's interesting and unusual that brother and sister are both footballers, and Sone's experience shows how things are different for men than for women in football.

2. Accept any reasoned explanation for using a fact file, e.g. 'The fact file picks out some of the most important information about Eniola, so you can see it at a glance. It helps sum things up'.

3. The quotes are 'What sport does is give you those experiences – which are real' and 'You are going to fail in sport, you are going to win sometimes, you are going to be criticised, you are going to be applauded – so it gives you … well, it's certainly given me anyway, those real-life experiences that make you bulletproof.' Accept any reasoned explanation for using direct quotations, e.g. 'The quote helps us to understand what motivates Eniola because we're reading her own words. It sounds like speech, and this makes it feel as though she's really speaking to the reader'. (Award one mark for identifying the quote, one for explaining what it adds.)

Word meanings

1. determination.

2. a) doing better than b) combining c) have to put up with

3. thrilling, barriers, salary, attention

Summarise

1. Early Career

2. Accept any reasonable sentence that sums up the main point of the paragraph without unnecessary detail, e.g. 'Unlike her brother, who was always a professional footballer, Eniola had to combine study and work with her football career'.

3. Accept any reasonable sentences that sum up the main points required, without unnecessary detail, e.g. a) 'Despite having to study and work hard alongside her early football career, Eniola has achieved success'. b) 'Women's football is becoming more popular'.

TEXT 3: POEM

Retrieval

1. true, false, true, true, false, false

2. A branch.

3. The grown-ups were chatting/gossiping and sharing drinks from a flask.

Inference (page 20)

1. a stone covered with soft moss

2. Accept any reasoned explanation with reference to the text, e.g. 'The mind-monsters are monsters that the children have imagined living in the stream. I think this because they are described as mind-monsters rather than real monsters'. (Award one mark for explaining the mind-monsters, one for giving a reason.)

3. Accept any reasoned response, e.g. 'I think the narrator of the poem is an adult looking back, because the poem is in the past tense and it says 'It flowed through our childhood', which sounds more like an adult talking than a child'. (Award one mark for a sensible description of the narrator, one for explaining their views.)

Inference (page 21)

1. It had a little waterfall or a place where the water moved quickly.

2. The teetering tightrope-walkers were the children crossing the stream on the branch. Accept any reasoned explanation of why these words are used, e.g. 'It's an effective description because it shows how the children had to balance very carefully on the branch across the stream'. (Award one mark for explaining the phrase, one for explaining why it's used.)

3. The children pitied the grown-ups because they couldn't enjoy the stream in the same imaginative way that the children did, so the grown-ups' world seemed small and a bit boring compared with the children's world. Accept any reasoned answer explaining why the student agrees or disagrees with this, e.g. 'I agree, because the grown-ups were only chatting and drinking tea, while the children were having fun exploring'. (Award one mark for identifying the meaning of the lines, one for explaining their own reaction.)

Word meanings

1. a) fish b) lying in wait c) walked through water

2. places where the stream is wide

3. shallows, tangle, creaking, nibbled

Language for effect

1. Any two of these lines, with underlining as shown: 'Mind-monsters in the deeps', 'For teetering tightrope-walkers', 'The lurking crocodile log', 'Were nibbled by tiny teeth', 'Mud-streaked, moss-flecked, twig-snagged', 'Story-mazed, stream-charmed'.

2. Accept any answer that explains the phrases, e.g. ''Ripple-voiced' shows us that the water of the stream was rippling, not still, and it made a sound as it moved, 'light-dancing' suggests that the sunlight is shining on the ripples of the stream'.

3. The lists are 'We followed it, mapped it, / Named its broads and shallows', 'Waded, splashed, climbed, fished', 'Mud-streaked, moss-flecked, twig-snagged, / Story-mazed, stream-charmed'. Accept any one or more of these. Accept any answer that gives reasons for effectiveness, e.g. 'I think the list is effective because it tells you very quickly about all the different things the children were doing'. (Award one mark for identifying list, one for giving opinion, one for giving reasons.)

Summarise

1. Accept any clear explanation of the main message, not including unnecessary detail, e.g. 'The main message is that the children loved the stream and spent a lot of time exploring it with their imaginations as well as physically'.

2. Accept any reasoned explanation of the title that is in keeping with the text, e.g. ''Our World' is the stream, and the poem shows how the children explored and mapped it'.

3. Accept any title that reflects what the poem is about, e.g. 'Our special stream'.

4. Accept any summing up of the main message of the whole poem (including the ending), e.g. 'Children can notice and enjoy things about the world that adults sometimes miss'.

TEXT 4: FICTION

Retrieval (page 27)

1. A water vole

2. a) early morning. b) complain sleepily.
   c) his mother catches him.

3. He knows that he has been told not to go to the river on his own.

Retrieval (page 28)

1. false, unknown, false, true, unknown, true

2. 'Her whiskers were stiff with disapproval.'

3. Accept any accurately written descriptive paragraph of at least two sentences, that draw on evidence about the setting that can be found in the text. (Award one mark for an accurate description, one for describing two or more features of the setting, one for picking up on text evidence.)

Inference (page 29)

1. Sometimes strict, but she wants her children to stay safe and have fun.

2. He doesn't want his mother to know he was about to go outside.

3. Accept any answer that shows understanding of the fact that Sylvan has been waiting for a long time to go to the Great River, and he is going to do this today.

Inference (page 30)

1. Accept any reasonable answer that is explained with reference to the text, e.g. 'I don't think Sylvan's mother believes him, because she can see he's looking guilty, and she says 'Hmm', which sounds as if she doesn't believe what he's just said'. (Award one mark for giving a reasonable point of view, one for explaining it with reference to the text.)

2. Accept any reasonable answer that the student has inferred from the context, implying that they are protesting because Sylvan is disturbing them in their sleep.

3. Accept any accurately written character profile of at least three sentences, including information about Sylvan's appearance, personality and family relationships that is in line with the text.

Word meanings

1. sad.

2. intertwined: twisted together, lulled: calmed, stole: crept quietly, surveyed: looked at

3. Accept any accurate description in the student's own words, e.g. hesitated: 'paused', vastness: 'huge size', stirred: 'moved lightly'

Prediction

1. Accept any accurately written conversation that is believable in the context of the story and the characters, e.g. '"Wake up! Hurry!" said Sylvan. "Mother says we can go out to the river!" "What?" said his brother sleepily, and then he realised what Sylvan

had just said. "The river? Brilliant! Come on, you lot, we'd better get going as quickly as we can!"'

2. Accept any credible prediction that draws on the student's knowledge of Sylvan's character, e.g. he is impetuous so he might get separated from the others and might have an adventure on his own, or get lost. (Award one mark for saying what might happen, one for this being believable in the context of Sylvan's character, one for writing a full paragraph.)

TEXT 5: INFORMATION TEXT

Retrieval

1. we've always got them in our eyes.

2. a) reflex tears. b) stress hormones.
   c) would get dry and sore.

3. a) Crying tears of sadness rather than yelling loudly means you will probably not attract a predator who might eat you.
   b) Crying tears of joy can create a connection between people, which is good for society's survival.

Inference

1. Accept any reasoned response that is in keeping with the text, e.g. 'Because there is no clear physical reason why emotional tears are useful'.

2. Accept any reasoned response that is in keeping with the text, e.g. I don't think it is known for certain, because the text says 'Some people think', and 'Whether this is true or not'. (Award one mark for an opinion, one for reasons connected with the text.)

3. Accept any appropriate description of a situation, e.g. where something has got into the eye or irritated it. The student should comment that the tears would be helpful because they would help stop the eye from getting sore, and/or wash away whatever was irritating it. (Award one mark for description, one for explaining why the tears are helpful.)

Word meanings

1. present: there in a particular place, irritated: inflamed or sore, produce: create or make, triggered: set off or started.

2. sends.

3. helplessness or vulnerability, upset, relaxed, sending or communicating.

Make connections

1. a) They are all questions.
   b) Accept any reasonable answer that is explained, e.g. 'Yes, they are effective because they make the reader think about the question that is going to be answered in the section'.

2. a) The bullet points give information about the different types of tears.
   b) Accept any reasoned answer, e.g. 'The author probably wanted the information about the three types of tears to stand out clearly and be easy to compare, so bullet points are useful for this. This is the only place in the text where different types of something are compared, so bullet points are not needed elsewhere'.

3. a) The first paragraph introduces the topic of the whole text.

   b) Accept any reasoned response, e.g. 'I think it makes an effective introduction because it gives some general information about the topic, and sets up the question that is answered in the rest of the text'.

Summarise

1. The Reasons for Our Tears

2. Accept any clear sentence that sums up the main idea without unnecessary detail, e.g. 'There might be an advantage in shedding tears and crying quietly, because it wouldn't attract predators'.

3. Accept any clear sentence that sums up the main idea without unnecessary detail, e.g. 'It's natural to cry at strong happy emotions, and maybe happy tears have an advantage in that they can bring people together'.

Published by Pearson Education Limited, 80 Strand, London, WC2R 0RL.

www.pearsonschoolsandfecolleges.co.uk

Text © Pearson Education Limited 2016
Edited by Jane Cotter
Typeset by Jouve India Private Limited
Produced by Elektra Media
Original illustrations © Pearson Education Limited 2016
Illustrated by Elektra Media
Cover illustration by Ana Albero

The right of Catherine Baker to be identified as author of this work has been asserted by her in accordance with the Copyright, Designs and Patents Act 1988.

First published 2016

19 18 17 16
10 9 8 7 6 5 4 3 2 1

British Library Cataloguing in Publication Data
A catalogue record for this book is available from the British Library

ISBN 978 1 292 14595 2

Printed in Italy by L.E.G.O. S.p.A.

Acknowledgements
We are grateful to the following for permission to reproduce copyright material:

Text
Text 1 extract from *The Scarecrow and his Servant* Random House (Pullman, P. 2004), World rights excluding US and Canada. Used by permission.

Text 2 quote from Eniola Aluko: I won't be paid the same as Wayne Rooney, because I'm not Wayne Rooney. https://www.theguardian.com/football/2016/jun/11/eniola-aluko-i-wont-be-paid-the-same-as-wayne-rooney-because-im-not-wayne-rooney, Hannah Ellis-Petersen, The Guardian, June 11, 2016.

Text 3 poem *Mapping Our World from Orange Silver Sausage: Poems Without Rhymes*, Walker Books Ltd (Carter J. and Denton, G.). Used by permission of Linda Newbery.

Text 4 extract from *The River Singers*, Oxford University Press (Moorhouse, T), © Tom Moorhouse 2013. Reprinted by permission of Oxford University Press.

Picture credits
The publisher would like to thank the following for their kind permission to reproduce their photographs:

Alamy Images: Cal Sport Media 10, Tony Henshaw 9; **Shutterstock.com:** Chepko Danil Vitalevich 33

All other images © Pearson Education